HERCULES

STEVE BARLOW + STEVE SKIDMORE
ART BY ANDREW TUNNEY

EDGE
FRANKLIN WATTS

LONDON·SYDNEY

Franklin Watts
First published in Great Britain in 2018
by The Watts Publishing Group

Text © Steve Barlow and Steve Skidmore 2018
Illustrations © Andrew Tunney 2018
Cover design: Peter Scoulding
Executive Editor: Adrian Cole

ISBN 978 1 4451 5228 8
ebook ISBN 978 1 4451 5229 5
Library ebook ISBN 978 1 4451 5230 1

1 3 5 7 9 10 8 6 4 2

Printed and bound by CPI Group (UK) Ltd, Croydon, CR0 4YY

Franklin Watts
An imprint of
Hachette Children's Group
Part of The Watts Publishing Group
Carmelite House
50 Victoria Embankment
London EC4Y 0DZ

An Hachette UK Company
www.hachette.co.uk

www.franklinwatts.co.uk

How to be a Legend

Throughout the ages, great men and women have performed deeds so mighty that even though history has forgotten them, their names have passed into legend.

You could be one of them.

In this book, you are Hercules, the hero of the adventure. You must make decisions that will affect how the adventure unfolds.

Each section of this book is numbered. At the end of most sections, you will have to make a choice. The choice you make will take you to a different section of the book.

Some of your choices will help you to complete the adventure successfully. But choose carefully, some of your decisions could be fatal!

If you fail, then start the adventure again and learn from your mistake.

If you choose wisely, you will succeed in your quest.

Are you ready to be a Hero? Have you got what it takes to become a Legend?

You are Hercules, a hero living in ancient Greece. You are known for your great strength and courage. You have had many adventures, fighting and defeating monstrous creatures, such as the nine-headed hydra and the Nemean lion.

The goddess Hera hates you and is always trying to place you in perilous situations, which she hopes you will not survive. Luckily, the goddess Athena likes you and helps you avoid Hera's traps.

As part of your latest adventure, you and Hylas, your arms-bearer, have joined the crew of the Argo to help another hero, Jason, in his quest to find the Golden Fleece. With the other Argonauts, you have spent days at sea, battling the storms created by Hera's brother, Poseidon, god of the sea.

Go to 1.

1

The storm rages as the Argo is battered by the wind and waves. You and the Argonauts are clinging on for your lives, when the ship's lookout cries, "Land ahead!"

You peer into the storm and can just make out the coastline of the land of Mysia. You know that this land is populated by many strange and dangerous creatures.

As the waves crash over the Argo, Jason seeks your advice. "Should we make for the shore?" he asks.

To advise Jason to head for land, go to 34.
To advise him to carry on, go to 19.

2

You place your blade against the centaur's neck. "If you know where my servant has been taken and tell me, I will spare your life," you say.

"I do not know where he has been taken," replies the centaur. "But I can tell you who does. You must travel to the Mountains of the East and seek the lair of Arachne, the spider-woman. She can tell you more."

You release the centaur from your grip and he gallops away.

Go to 35.

3

"Hylas is lost forever," you say to Jason. "I will join you."

You take your place on the Argo, but in your heart you know you have made a bad choice. The Argonauts stare at you as you sail away from Mysia. You hang your head in shame. You are no hero.

Cowards can never become legends! Go back to 1.

4

You dive into the raging water to try to rescue your companions. However, despite your brave efforts, they are sucked down into the icy depths. Waves crash over your head as you try to swim back towards the Argo, but even your strength is no match against the power of Poseidon's domain.

Water pours into your lungs and you sink into the blackness of the sea.

Begin your adventure again, and go back to 1.

5

You turn away from the pool, and the air is suddenly filled with ear-piercing screeches. You spin around. The nymphs are transforming into harpies!

The fearsome creatures fly towards you, slashing at your body with their sharp talons. Desperately, you try to fight them, but there are too many, even for a great fighter like you. The attack continues until finally you sink to the ground, lifeless.

Begin your adventure again. Go to 1.

6

You make your way to the opening of the cave and climb up onto the ledge.

"Keto!" you cry out. "Show yourself!"

At that moment, the tentacled body of a great sea monster emerges from the cave.

In an instant, you leap from the ledge, sword drawn and thrust the blade into the creature's grotesque head. Keto screams in agony as you continue your deadly attack. Her tentacles try to grab at you, but you are too quick for the wounded creature.

You raise your sword and with one final blow, Keto crashes into the sea, dead.

You leap from the creature's body and hurry over to Hylas. You take the chains in your hands and break them, freeing your grateful arms-bearer.

Go to 50.

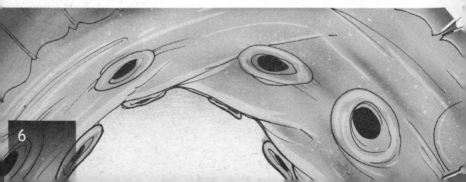

7

You take aim at the target and let fly. However, the breeze takes your arrow off course and it just misses to the left of the target.

"We shoot again!" cries Chiron. He shoots and this time he hits the target. "Your turn!" he says.

You pull back the string and let loose. The arrow again misses the target. The centaurs laugh. "You lose, and now you will pay for killing Nessus!"

To plead for your life, go to 18.
To attack the centaurs, go to 28.

8

You stagger to the prow of the ship and hold out your arms. "Fight me!" you challenge the god.

The storm begins to subside as Poseidon stares at you in disbelief. "Do you dare to challenge me, mortal?"

"I am no mere mortal," you say defiantly. "I am Hercules!"

The god laughs. "Hercules? My sister Hera has spoken about you. I think she does not care for you."

"And I do not care for her. Will you fight me or not?"

The sea is now calm as Poseidon shakes his head. "It is a fight you cannot win," he says.

To call Poseidon a coward, go to 30.

To ask him to let you head for the shore, go to 16.

9

You peer into the depths of the cavern and see the bloated figure of Arachne, half-spider, half-woman. She is surrounded by her brood of spider children.

"I am Hercules," you say.

"And what brings you here, Hercules?" Arachne asks.

"I am searching for my arms-bearer, Hylas, who was taken by harpies," you reply. "Do you know where he is?"

Arachne laughs. "Of course. My children are spread across the face of the Earth. Nothing happens that we do not know. But why should I tell you? What can you give me in return?"

To threaten Arachne, go to 46.

To bargain with her, go to 31.

"Greetings, noble centaurs," you say. "I am Hercules."

Their leader trots forward. "I am Chiron, king of the centaurs, and we know who you are. You are the one who killed our brother, Nessus."

You nod. "What you say is true, but only because he kidnapped my wife."

Chiron considers your words. "Why are you here, Hercules?"

You tell him about Hylas. "Do you know where he might have been taken?" you ask.

"Perhaps we do," replies the centaur. "But we will only tell you if you undertake a challenge. If you are successful, we will help you in your quest. If not, then you will pay for killing Nessus."

"What is this challenge?" you ask.

"It is quite simple. An archery contest against me," replies Chiron.

If you wish to take the challenge, go to 25.
If you wish to fight the centaurs, go to 28.

11

You remember Poseidon's words to you about a breeze from the south. You know this comes from your right, so you must allow for the wind when you shoot.

You aim to the right of the target and let loose your arrow. It catches on the breeze but hits the target dead centre.

"I win!" you say. "And now you must tell me what you know about Hylas."

"You must travel to the Mountains of the East," replies Chiron. "Seek the lair of Arachne, the spider-woman. She can tell you more."

Before you can ask any more questions, the centaurs gallop away.

Go to 35.

12

Drawing your sword, you creep up on the gryphon and before it can react, you leap on its back and hold the sharp blade against its neck.

"If you wish to live, then you will fly me to the cave of Keto. If not, then your blood will be spilt on this rocky path."

Carefully, the gryphon nods in agreement and you are soon airborne, hanging onto the creature's back.

The gryphon's wings cut through the air as you travel across the great plains to the lair of Keto.

After many hours of travelling, you arrive at a craggy coastline, where far below, you see a figure chained to a rock.

"Hylas!" you cry and order the gryphon to land. You dismount and let the creature fly away.

To free Hylas immediately, go to 37.
To make sure everything is safe, go to 20.

13

You draw your sword. "Tell me where Hylas is or you will feel my blade!"

"Do not threaten us!" screams one of the nymphs, and the air is filled with screeching as the nymphs transform into harpies.

They fly at you, clawing at your body with their deadly, razor-sharp talons. You are helpless against these creatures of nightmare, and seconds later your lifeless body lies sprawled on the ground.

You shouldn't have threatened such beings! Go back to 1.

14

"You should not have attacked me," you tell the centaur and you are soon on your way, leaving your enemies lying dead.

You arrive at the glade where Hylas was taken and search for clues, but can find nothing. Suddenly there is a crash of thunder and a flash of lightning. When you open your eyes, you are shocked to see the goddess Hera standing before you.

She laughs scornfully. "There is nothing to find here, Hercules! The centaurs knew where Hylas had been taken and you have killed them. Now you will never find him, no matter how far and wide you travel. May you feel sorrow and shame for the rest of your days." With those words, the goddess vanishes.

You sink to your knees in despair, for you know she is right.

You should not have been so bloodthirsty! Go back to 1.

15

As one, the gryphons suddenly speed towards you, screeching with rage.

Before you can defend yourself, one of the creatures smashes into you with its sharp talons. The other gryphons join in the attack and you drop to the ground, helpless to fight off the horde. Their sharp beaks snap at your skin, before you pass out into the merciful blackness of death.

That was not the stuff of legend! Go back to 1.

"I know this," you reply, "but I also know that if I do nothing we will all die. If you will not fight me, then show mercy and allow us to make for the shoreline."

The god considers before replying. "Although my sister Hera will be angry when she hears that I have spared you, I will reward your bravery and allow you safe passage."

"We thank you for your mercy," you say.

"I will give you a final piece of advice," continues the god. "Take heed of the breeze from the south and aim right."

Before you can ask Poseidon what he means by this, the god disappears beneath the waves.

"We should make for land," you say to Jason. "We need to repair the Argo and take on provisions. But we should be on our guard. Mysia is a dangerous country."

Go to 38.

"I will do this if you first show me where he is," you say.

Arachne nods. "Children, show Hercules where Hylas is." Her brood obey and begin to weave a map out of silken threads. Within minutes it is finished.

"Hylas has been taken to the cave of the sea monster Keto, mother of the Gorgons," Arachne tells you. "And now you must keep your side of the bargain."

"I will do my best," you say. "Athena, I call upon your help."

There is a blinding flash of light and the goddess appears. You tell her of the bargain you made with Arachne, but the goddess shakes her head. "You ask too much, Hercules. Arachne offended me; I will not return her to human form." The goddess vanishes.

Arachne turns on you in rage. "You have failed to give me what I want! Children, kill him!"

To try and escape from the cavern, go to 33.

To attack the spiders, go to 42.

18

You drop your bow and kneel on the ground.

"Noble creatures, Nessus deserved his punishment. He was shaming the good name of the centaurs by his actions."

Chiron considers your words. "What you say is true. I will spare your life. However, we will not help you with your quest to find Hylas."

Before you can protest, the centaurs gallop away, leaving you wondering where you should head next.

Go to 35.

19

"Mysia is a dangerous land," you say. "We should continue with the journey."

Jason trusts your judgement. "We carry on!" he orders. Some of the other Argonauts mutter their disapproval.

Suddenly, the gigantic figure of Poseidon emerges from out of the depths of the sea. The waves crash over the deck as the god of the sea roars in anger.

The Argo is caught in this supernatural blast of

wind and spins out of control, the mast groaning
and the sails tearing.

If you want to head to shore, go to 49.
If you wish to carry on, go to 43.

20

You stand looking around for signs of danger.

"Hylas, who has put you in chains?" you ask.

"The goddess Hera bound me to this rock
and told the sea monster Keto to guard me,"
he replies.

"Where is Keto?" you ask.

"I don't know," replies Hylas.

You look carefully around the shoreline. A dark
cave lies next to the rock where Hylas is chained.
A small rocky ledge juts out above the opening,
but there is no sign of Keto.

To head towards the cave, go to 6.
To free Hylas, go to 37.

21

You watch in horror as the nymphs transform
into harpies. They fly at you, baring their deadly
teeth and slashing at your body with their talons.

You try to fight them off, but the effects of the poppy flowers are too great. Hylas is dragged away as you drop to the floor, unconscious.

Hours later you wake up. It is dark and there is no sign of Hylas. You make your way back to the Argo and tell Jason what has happened.

"Where do you think these creatures will have taken him?" asks Jason.

You shake your head. "I do not know."

"The Argo is ready to depart on our quest to find the Golden Fleece," says Jason. "Will you come with us?"

If you wish to board the ship, go to 3.

If you wish to search for Hylas, go to 45.

22

Taking advantage of the gryphon's uncertainty, you make your way up the mountain path, keeping a wary eye on the creatures.

Ahead of you is the entrance to a cave. Great tattered webs choke the cave mouth, as if it is the lair of some monstrous spider.

If you wish to head into the cave, go to 40.

To continue up the path, go to 48.

As you search for the source of the laughter, a female figure suddenly appears from the depths of the pool. You watch in amazement as more figures emerge from beneath the water, laughing and beckoning you towards them.

"Who or what are these creatures?" asks Hylas.

"They are water nymphs," you reply.

"Welcome, Hercules and Hylas."

"How do you know who we are?" you ask.

"Everyone knows of the famous hero Hercules. Come and talk to us."

"You said we should be on our guard in this land," says Hylas. "We should leave this place, immediately."

To talk to the nymphs, go to 32.
To leave the glade, go to 5.

24

You take a torch from the cavern wall and move towards the hanging sacks.

In the flickering light, you see that they are not what you thought — they are dead bodies wrapped in silk cocoons!

A voice suddenly rings out across the cavern. "Who dares enter the lair of Arachne, the spider-woman?"

To talk to Arachne, go to 9.
To escape from the cavern, go to 33.

25

"Very well, I accept," you say. You prepare your bow as a target is set against an olive tree some distance away.

"We stand in the west and shoot at the target in the east," says Chiron. "The best of three shots."

The centaur shoots first and hits the target as do you with your first shot. Again, Chiron takes aim and scores a direct hit. You take your second shot and strike the target.

As Chiron takes his third shot, you feel the

wind pick up, and the centaur's arrow misses the target to the left. "A breeze from the south, I think," he says. "If you hit the target, you win. If not, we shoot again."

Something stirs in your memory as you take aim at the target.

If you wish to aim at the target, go to 7.

If you wish to aim to the right of the target, go to 11.

If you wish to aim to the left of the target, go to 39.

26

You dive onto the deck and hide behind the ship's mast as Poseidon hurls his trident. The deadly weapon rips into the Argo's hull, breaking the ship apart.

You and the Argonauts plunge into the sea. You try to swim towards land, but the storm is too great. Waves crash over you, filling your lungs with water. Soon your struggles are over as you sink into blackness of Poseidon's realm.

Your adventure has finished almost before it began! Go back to 1.

27

You nock an arrow to your bowstring, take aim and shoot. The arrow merely bounces off the creature's hide. It turns around and snaps at you with its beak. You rush forward and somehow manage to squeeze past the creature.

However, the gryphon's screeching alerts the other gryphons flying overhead.

Go to 15.

28

Before the centaurs can react, you nock an arrow to your bowstring and let fly. While your first arrow is still in the air, you fire another. Your aim is true and two of the creatures drop down dead.

The other two centaurs shoot back at you, but you manage to avoid their arrows. As you nock another arrow to your bowstring, the two remaining creatures charge towards you.

To continue to use your bow, go to 41.
To fight them with your sword, go to 36.

29

You draw your bow and shoot at the gryphons. However, the arrows merely bounce off their armoured hides. Screeching with rage, the fearsome creatures head towards you.

To use your strength to overcome the creatures, go to 15.
To defend yourself with your sword, go to 44.

30

"If you will not fight me, then you are a coward..."

"You dare to call me a coward? You go too far, Hercules!" roars Poseidon, smashing his hand down on the sea. Waves crash over the deck, sending several of the Argonauts over the side and into the raging water. Hanging onto the ship's rail, you look up to see the god preparing to throw his deadly trident.

Go to 26.

31

"What is it that I can give you?" you ask.

"I was turned into this form by your protector, the goddess Athena," Arachne replies. "You must call upon her to return me to wholly human form. If you do that I will tell you where Hylas has been taken."

You know it will be very difficult to ask for Athena's help.

If you agree to Arachne's demands, go to 17.

If you don't, go to 46.

32

"I am not afraid of these creatures," you laugh. "Come, Hylas, let us talk with them."

You head over to the pool. One of the nymphs holds out a golden cup. "Come, drink with us," she says.

You take the cup and drink from it. Within seconds you begin to feel light-headed. Your vision becomes blurred and you drop to your knees, the cup tumbling from your limp hand.

"What have you done?" you gasp.

"We soaked poppy flowers in the water," laughs the nymph. "And now you will sleep and we will take Hylas!"

To try and escape, go to 5.
To try and rescue Hylas, go to 21.

33

You turn around and run into the tunnel. However, in your haste to escape, you blunder into a different tunnel from the one you entered. You come to a sudden stop as you crash headlong into some sort of sticky net.

You try to struggle free, but you are stuck! You see a dark shape begin crawling towards you and you realise this is no net, it is a giant spider's web and you are trapped! The spider moves towards you, its deadly venom running down its open jaws.

You try to free yourself, but it is useless. The spider's jaws open and snap shut on your neck. You feel its venom course through your body, freezing your blood and your muscles.

You didn't get out of that sticky situation. Go back to 1.

34

"We should head for land," you cry, taking over the helm to steer through the raging seas.

As you swing the ship towards the shoreline, it is almost capsized as the figure of Poseidon, the god of the sea, emerges from out of the depths. The angry god holds out his trident, blocking the way to the shore.

If you still wish to try and get to land, go to 49.

If you wish to turn around, go to 43.

35

You decide to head towards the distant Mountains of the East.

After several days of hard travelling, you finally arrive and begin to make your way up the pass leading through the mountains.

As you head up the rocky pathway, you hear screeching. You glance upwards and see a flock of gryphons flying towards you, talons bared.

To wait and see what the gryphons will do, go to 15.

To shoot at the creatures, go to 29.

You draw your sword and rush at the oncoming
creatures. You manage to connect with the
first centaur and he crashes to the ground,
mortally wounded. You leap onto the back of the
remaining centaur. Desperately, he tries to shake
you off, but your grip is too strong and you force
him to the ground.

If you wish to spare the centaur, go to 2.
If you wish to kill your enemy, go to 14.

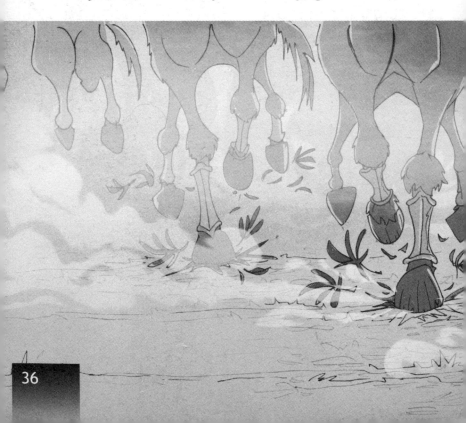

"I will free you from those chains," you say.

Hylas looks worried. "Be careful, master. The monster Keto could be nearby!"

Before you can react, a great sea monster rears up from out of the churning waves and in the blink of an eye, its great tentacles coil around your body, trapping you.

Desperately you try to free yourself, but even your great strength is not enough to break free from Keto's deadly embrace. Surely but slowly, your life is squeezed from your body.

You didn't get to grips with Keto! Go back to 1.

38

The Argo lays anchor in a bay off Mysia, and you and some the Argonauts make your way onto shore.

You and your arms-bearer, Hylas, head inland to search for food and water. You follow the course of a stream which eventually leads to a glade with a clear pool of water.

As you head towards the pool, you hear the sound of laughter. You look around, but there is no one in view. The laughter breaks out again. "What strange place is this?" Hylas asks.

"Mysia is a land of danger, be on your guard," you warn.

To head to the pool and gather water, go to 47.

To explore the glade, go to 23.

39

You take aim to the left of the target and let fly. You let out a cry of anguish as the arrow is caught by the breeze. It misses the target and hits a centaur in the chest.

"You did that on purpose!" cries Chiron.

Before you can proclaim your innocence, he pulls back his bowstring and shoots an arrow at you. It hits you and you drop to the ground. The other centaurs follow their leader's example and shoot at you, sending you to the next world.

You have paid the price for aiming badly! Go to 1.

40

You head into the cave and to your amazement see a flickering light ahead of you.

You make your way through the narrow, rocky tunnel and find yourself in a vast cavern, lit by flaming torches. A putrid, rotting smell fills the air and you can make out what look like large sacks hanging from the roof of the cavern.

To explore the cavern, go to 24.

To get out of the cavern immediately, go to 33.

41

You draw back your bowstring, but before you can shoot, the centaurs are upon you. They rear up, bringing their hooves crashing down on you.

Other centaurs appear and let fly their arrows and the deadly missiles pierce your chest, sending you crashing to the ground.

You have failed in your quest. Go back to 1.

42

You leap towards the silk cocoons hanging from the cavern's roof, and hold out the flaming torch. A cocoon catches fire. You push it towards another, and that too catches fire.

Before Arachne and her brood can react, the cavern is ablaze. The fiery cocoons drop down, setting alight to Arachne's children.

In the chaos, you race out of the tunnel. You make your way to the entrance, only to find a gryphon blocking your escape.

To shoot at the gryphon with your arrows, go to 27.

To sneak up on it and use your sword, go to 12.

43

"We will never make it to land," you cry as the waves crash over the deck. But before the Argo can escape from Poseidon's fury, you see the god aiming his deadly trident at the ship.

To take cover, go to 26.
To challenge the god to a fight, go to 8.

44

You draw your sword and stand poised ready to fight off the creatures. The leading gryphon dives at you, and you swing your sword aiming for its front legs. The blade slices through the bone and the creature veers away, screaming in agony.

A second gryphon takes up the fight and again you chop at its leg, severing it in two. It flies away, leaving the other gryphons circling above you, uncertain whether to attack or not.

To move up the mountain path, go to 22.
To wait for the gryphons to attack, go to 15.

"I must try to find Hylas," you tell Jason.

He nods. "I understand. Good luck, my friend. I hope your quest is successful." He hands you a bow, arrows and a sword. "You will need these."

You thank Jason and watch as the Argo sets
sail before heading back towards the glade where
Hylas was taken.

As you make your way along the dusty path,
you come to a sudden halt. Ahead of you are four
centaurs blocking your way. They are armed with
bows and arrows, which are all aimed at you.

To attack the centaurs, go to 28.
To talk to them, go to 10.

"I will give you and your brood the sharp blade of my sword and the deadly points of my arrows if you do not tell me where Hylas has been taken," you snarl.

"You dare to threaten me?" laughs Arachne. "Children, show this fool our power."

The cavern is suddenly filled by thousands of spiders dropping from the ceiling and pouring out from under the rocks. Before you can react, you are engulfed by them. Desperately you try to fight them off, but there are too many.

Within minutes you are encased in a cocoon of silk, hanging from the roof of the cavern.

It looks like you're on Arachne's dinner menu! Go back to 1.

47

As you head towards the pool, a whirlwind of dust and sand fills the air. You shield your eyes and when the wind dies down, Hylas has disappeared, and sitting by the pool is a group of six water nymphs.

"Where is Hylas?" you ask.

"Why should we know?" says one of the nymphs.

To threaten the nymphs, go to 13.
To leave the glade and search for Hylas, go to 5.

48

You continue up the path as the gryphons circle above you. It seems to you that they are communicating to each other. A feeling of unease passes through your body.

Go to 15.

49

The god of the sea sends waves crashing over the ship's deck. Some of the Argonauts are swept over the side into the raging torrent. You hear their cries for help. At that moment, you look up to see Poseidon pulling back his arm and aiming his trident at the Argo.

To try and rescue the Argonauts from the sea, go to 4.

To take cover, go to 26.

To challenge Poseidon to a fight, go to 8.

50

As Hylas thanks you, a shimmering light shines in the sky and the goddess Athena appears. "Well done," she says. "You have foiled Hera's plan."

You bow to your protector. "So Hera was behind Hylas's kidnapping by the nymphs?"

Athena smiles. "Yes — and she ordered the harpies to bring him here to use as bait. She hoped to lure you into the deadly grip of Keto. She underestimated you, though!"

Hylas laughs. "Truly, master, people through the ages will remember your mighty deeds. This story, like you, will go down in legend!"

You are Freya, a young goddess of the Vikings. You live in Asgard, home of the gods.

One day, Odin, the father of the gods, summons you to his great hall, Valhalla. Thor, the god of thunder stands beside him, head held low.

Odin addresses you. "I want Thor to deal with a rebellion of the Frost Giants," says Odin, "but he has lost Mjolnir, his magic hammer, and with it all of his powers."

You bow. "I will find Mjolnir and return it to Thor."

You call for your chariot, drawn by two enormous cats, and set off at once in search of Thor's magic hammer. With Odin's crows as your escort, you leave Asgard over Bifrost, the rainbow bridge that leads to Earth…

Continue the adventure in:
IHERO LEGENDS
FREYA

About the 2Steves

"The 2Steves" are
Britain's most popular
writing double act
for young people,
specialising in comedy
and adventure. They
perform regularly in schools and libraries,
and at festivals, taking the power of words
and story to audiences of all ages.

Together they have written many books,
including the *I HERO Immortals* and *iHorror* series.

About the illustrator:
Andrew Tunney (aka 2hands)

Andrew is a freelance artist and writer based in
Manchester, UK. He has worked in illustration, character
design, comics, print, clothing and live-art. His work
has been featured by Comics Alliance, ArtSlant Street,
DigitMag, The Bluecoat, Starburst and Forbidden Planet.
He earned the nickname "2hands" because he can draw
with both hands at once. He is not ambidextrous; he just
works hard.

Also in the I HERO Legends series:

ATHENA	BEOWULF	KING ARTHUR	ROBIN HOOD
978 1 4451 5234 9 pb	978 1 4451 5225 7 pb	978 1 4451 5231 8 pb	978 1 4451 5183 0 pb
978 1 4451 5235 6 ebook	978 1 4451 5226 4 ebook	978 1 4451 5232 5 ebook	9/8 1 4451 5184 7 ebook

Have you read the I HERO Atlantis Quest mini series?

MENACE FROM THE DEEP	OCEAN ALLIANCE	BATTLE FOR THE SEAS	ATLANTIS ASSAULT
978 1 4451 2867 2 pb	978 1 4451 2870 2 pb	978 1 4451 2876 4 pb	978 1 4451 2873 3 pb
978 1 4451 2868 9 ebook	978 1 4451 2871 9 ebook	978 1 4451 2877 1 ebook	978 1 4451 2874 0 ebook

Also by the 2Steves...

978 1 4451 4081 0 pb
978 1 4451 4082 7 eBook

You are the last Dragon Warrior.
A dark, evil force stirs within the
Iron Mines. Grull the Cruel's
army is on the march! YOU must
stop Grull.

978 1 4451 4088 9 pb
978 1 4451 4087 2 eBook

You are a noble mermaid —
your father is King Edmar.
The Tritons are attacking your home
of Coral City. YOU must save the Merrow
people by finding the Lady of the Sea.

978 1 4451 4084 1 pb
978 1 4451 4085 8 eBook

You are Olympian, a superhero.
Your enemy, Doctor Robotic,
is turning people into mind slaves.
Now YOU must put a stop to his
plans before it's too late!

978 1 4451 3958 6 pb
978 1 4451 3961 6 eBook

You are a young wizard.
The evil Witch Queen has captured
Prince Bron. Now YOU must rescue
him before she takes control of
Nine Mountain kingdom!